C000231373

Spelling Today
for ages 10-11

...includes words, spelling patterns and
spelling rules recommended for
Year 6 pupils.

How to use this book:

1. Look at the rules and words featured on the right-hand pages.

2. Turn over the page to look at each word on the left-hand page.

3. Cover the word with the flap, then write the word.

4. Uncover the word to check that you haven't made a mistake.

5. Write the word again for extra practice.

Beginnings and endings

Some sets of words all have the same beginning …

… and some sets all have the same ending.

Fill the gaps in the sentences with the correct words.

beginning:　**aero**　　words:　aeroplane　aerodynamic

The car went so fast because it was very ＿＿＿＿＿＿＿ .

We flew to Spain on an ＿＿＿＿＿＿＿ .

beginning:　**aqua**　　words:　aquarium　aquatic

Only plants which are ＿＿＿＿＿＿＿ will survive in an ＿＿＿＿＿＿＿ .

beginning:　**audi**　　words:　audience　audition　audible

I went for an ＿＿＿＿＿＿＿ for a part in the school play.

The voice of the pilot was barely ＿＿＿＿＿＿＿ above the sound of the engine.

The ＿＿＿＿＿＿＿ clapped very loudly when the show finished.

Practise these words which all have the ending **ence**.

difference	absence	experience	independence	confidence

Practise these words which all have the ending **ance**.

distance	guidance	balance	nuisance	importance

3

Step 1	Step 2	Step 3
Look and learn, then cover the word with the flap.	Write the word, then see if it's correct.	Write the word again. Say it as you write it.
aeroplane		
aquarium		
aquaplane		
audience		
audition		
difference		
absence		
experience		
independence		
distance		
guidance		
nuisance		
importance		
important		
importantly		
unimportant		

4

Beginnings and endings

In the word-bank there are four sets of words which go together.

Find the sets which have matching beginnings or endings.

word-bank

pupil   angel   submarine   telephone
cancel   television   pencil   submit   cruel
label   telepathy   telecom   subject   quarrel   telegraph
subway   April   submerse   until   council

All of these words begin with:

All of these words end with:

All of these words begin with:

All of these words end with:

5

Step 1	Step 2	Step 3
Look and learn, then cover the word with the flap.	Write the word, then see if it's correct.	Write the word again. Say it as you write it.
submerse		
subway		
submarine		
subject		
angel		
cancel		
cruel		
quarrel		
label		
council		
until		
pupil		
television		
telephone		
telegraph		
telecommunications		

6

que, qua and qui

Sort the words in the word-bank into the three sets.

Notice that **q** is always followed by **u**.

word-bank

oblique   squint   antique   quality   unique
quarrel   sequin   quantity   squirrel
quintuplet   sequence   quarry   squash   queue   qualify   cheque   mosque
disqualify   technique   square   quarter

Words with **qua**	Words with **que**	Words with **qui**

Can you think of any words with **quo** ?

Step 1	Step 2	Step 3
Look and learn, then cover the word with the flap.	Write the word, then see if it's correct.	Write the word again. Say it as you write it.
quality		
antique		
quintuplet		
quantity		
quite		
quiet		
queue		
qualify		
cheque		
unique		
technique		
square		
quarter		
sequence		
oblique		
squirrel		

8

Word families

Look in the word-bank to find words containing **ure** to fill the gaps in this passage.

Look for other word families in the word-bank and within the passage.

word-bank

vicar   creature   agriculture   regular
calendar   temperature   familiar   adventure   puncture   popular   fixture
mixture   signature   guitar   prime   sugar   primary   departure

Yesterday I had a very peculiar _____. An unfamiliar _____ was

sitting in my front garden. It seemed to be some sort of a _____ between a

human and a gorilla. The _____ was very high so the animal tried to cool

down in the garden pond. Unfortunately it made a _____ in the plastic

pond liner and all of the water escaped. I was a bit frightened so I decided to make a

quick _____ .

Which **ure** words are in the word-bank but were not needed for the gaps?

_____   _____   _____

Find all the words which end in **ar**, either in the passage or in the word-bank:

_____   _____   _____   _____

_____   _____   _____   _____   _____

Find all the words which start with **prim**:

_____   _____   _____

Step 1	Step 2	Step 3
Look and learn, then cover the word with the flap.	Write the word, then see if it's correct.	Write the word again. Say it as you write it.
adventure		
agriculture		
signature		
temperature		
creature		
puncture		
fixture		
prime		
primary		
peculiar		
familiar		
calendar		
regular		
popular		
vicar		
sugar		

ph and auto

There are quite a lot of words ...

... where **ph** makes a sound like the letter f.

Practise the word here:

The word **phobia** means a fear of something. →

Claustrophobia means a fear of confined spaces. →

Arachnophobia means a fear of spiders. →

Agoraphobia means a fear of open spaces. →

Practise the sets of words:

ph words

dolphin

pamphlet

pharmacy

sphere

atmosphere

emphasise

nephew

apostrophe

graph words

graphic

photograph

photography

biography

autograph

other auto words

automobile

autobiography

automatic

Step 1 Look and learn, then cover the word with the flap.	Step 2 Write the word, then see if it's correct.	Step 3 Write the word again. Say it as you write it.
automatic		
autobiography		
automobile		
autograph		
claustrophobia		
claustrophobic		
photograph		
dolphin		
apostrophe		
sphere		
atmosphere		
pamphlet		
pharmacy		
nephew		
graphic		
photographic		

our and or

Choose the correct word to fill each gap:

colour	
horror	What _____ is your _____ ?
calculator	What is your _____ _____ story?
favourite	

neighbours	
escalator	I saw a famous _____ on the _____ .
actor	The _____ of my _____ is very bad!
behaviour	

visitor	
doctor	The telephone _____ put my call through to the _____ .
operator	The _____ arrived in the _____ on a sailing boat.
harbour	

Practise these words:

labour	_____	accelerator	_____	interior	_____
flavour	_____	equator	_____	junior	_____
favour	_____	solicitor	_____	senior	_____

In America they spell some words differently to the way we spell them.

For example, they spell colour, c o l o r .

Step 1 Look and learn, then cover the word with the flap.	Step 2 Write the word, then see if it's correct.	Step 3 Write the word again. Say it as you write it.
colour		
favour		
favourite		
harbour		
behaviour		
neighbours		
senior		
junior		
interior		
exterior		
doctor		
operator		
equator		
horror		
calculator		
visitor		

ary, ery, al and ex

Stationary means not moving.

Stationery is a name given to writing materials such as paper and envelopes.

Some people get the spellings of stationary and stationery mixed up. One clue is that stationery and paper both have er in them.

Practise the sets of words:

ary words

dictionary

necessary

stationary

ordinary

extraordinary

Notice that extraordinary is made up of **extra** and **ordinary**.

al words

royal

pedal

medical

actual

actually

general

generally

ex words

export

expert

expertise

experience

experiment

extend

Step 1	Step 2	Step 3
Look and learn, then cover the word with the flap.	Write the word, then see if it's correct.	Write the word again. Say it as you write it.
stationery		
stationary		
dictionary		
royalty		
pedal		
necessary		
unnecessary		
expert		
medical		
expertise		
ordinary		
extraordinary		
experience		
actually		
experiment		
general		

16

re

Some words have an er sound at the end ...

... but the spelling is **re**.

Choose the correct word to fill each gap:

metre
centimetre
centimetres
millimetres

One hundred _____ make one _____.

One thousand _____ make one _____.

Ten _____ make one _____.

theatre
centre
acre

The middle of a circle is called the _____.

The farmer sold an _____ of land.

I saw a pantomime at the _____.

More **re** endings to practise:

fibre _____   litre _____   millilitre _____

Words with **re** at the beginning:

reply	replies	repeat	repetition	remember

replay	rewind	reminder	return	restore

pre words and cred words

preview		prehistoric		credit	
previous		previously		credible	
prevent		prevention		incredible	

17

Step 1 Look and learn, then cover the word with the flap.	Step 2 Write the word, then see if it's correct.	Step 3 Write the word again. Say it as you write it.
metre		
centimetre		
millimetre		
litre		
millilitre		
centre		
central		
theatre		
theatrical		
remember		
replies		
previous		
previously		
prevention		
prehistoric		
incredible		

18

Number prefixes

Some words have a prefix …

… which shows a number.

For example, **bi** means two…

…so bicycle begins with **bi** because it has two wheels.

one: mono or uni   two: bi or du   three: tri

Sort the words in the word-bank into the correct sets:

word-bank

monocle   tricycle   trident   biplane
triplet   biceps   monologue   duo   unicorn   duet
union   monopoly   bicentenary   dual   trio   monorail   tripod
triangle   binoculars   monosyllable   unicycle   bifocal   trinity   triangular

one	two	three

Step 1	Step 2	Step 3
Look and learn, then cover the word with the flap.	Write the word, then see if it's correct.	Write the word again. Say it as you write it.
monopoly		
monorail		
union		
unity		
united		
bicycle		
binoculars		
duet		
duplicate		
triangle		
triangular		
trinity		
trio		
triplet		
tricolour		
tripod		

More number prefixes

How many sides does a quadrilateral have?

Four.

four: quad or quart or tetra   five: quin or pent   six: hex or sex
seven: sept or hept   eight: oct   nine: non   ten: dec   hundred: cent

Sort the words in the word-bank into the correct sets:

word-bank

quadrilateral   sextet   quarter   decade
octagon (an eight-sided shape)   septet   quartet   pentagon   century   octet
decagon (a ten-sided shape)   nonagon (a nine-sided shape)   pentathlon   quintuplet
quadruple   quadruplet   quadruped   hexagon   heptagon (a seven-sided shape)
octopus   decathlon   centimetre   tetrahedron (a pyramid made of four triangles)   decimal

four

five

eight

hundred

six

nine

seven

ten

Name the shapes with:

4 sides

5 sides

6 sides

7 sides

8 sides

9 sides

10 sides

Step 1	Step 2	Step 3
Look and learn, then cover the word with the flap.	Write the word, then see if it's correct.	Write the word again. Say it as you write it.
quadrilateral		
quarter		
tetrahedron		
quartet		
quintet		
pentagon		
hexagon		
heptagon		
octagon		
hexagonal		
octagonal		
octopus		
decade		
decimal		
century		
centipede		

con

On this page we have lots of words beginning with **con** or containing **con**.

You could use a dictionary to find some more.

Copy the words, then choose the correct ones to fit the gaps in the sentences at the bottom of the page.

economy

contraflow

contradict

conversation

concert

condition

reconditioned

economical

congratulations

conservatory

confess

confession

consequences

conclude

condensation

conservation

continent

connection

The inside of the window was wet with   .

Traffic on the motorway was slowed down by a   system.

The big, glass   was built onto the back of the house.

Make sure that your pen is in good   for writing in the test.

It was more   to buy two packets of cornflakes because they were on special offer.

Step 1	Step 2	Step 3
Look and learn, then cover the word with the flap.	Write the word, then see if it's correct.	Write the word again. Say it as you write it.
congratulations		
conversation		
economy		
conservatory		
conservation		
continent		
continental		
connected		
connection		
contradiction		
confess		
confession		
condition		
conclude		
conclusion		
contents		

In the first set of words below, you can't hear the letter u.

In the second set of words you can hear the u very clearly.

Practise the words in both sets:

build	builder	built	building	antique	buy

biscuit	tongue	guess	guard	guest	shoulder

catalogue	guinea-pig	guarantee

include	inclusion	exclude	excluded	clue	glue

due	duet	during	pure	impure	sure

unsure	conclude	conclusion

Choose words from both sets to complete these sentences:

I was _____ that the house would fall down but the _____ told me that he had _____ it properly. He said it had a ten year _____. I was very pleased so I gave him a cup of tea and a _____. Then I looked through a _____ of very old, _____ furniture to choose what I wanted to _____.

Step 1	Step 2	Step 3
Look and learn, then cover the word with the flap.	Write the word, then see if it's correct.	Write the word again. Say it as you write it.
antique		
build		
builder		
building		
biscuit		
catalogue		
shoulder		
could		
should		
would		
conclusion		
glue		
pure		
sure		
guard		
guarantee		

ist, ology, ory and port

Archaeologists study archaeology!

They try to find out about the past by digging up ancient things.

Choose the correct word to fill each gap:

archaeology

zoology

biology

geology

Biologists are experts in _____, the study of plants and animals.

Geologists are experts in _____, the study of the rocks of which the earth is made.

Zoologists are experts in _____, the study of animals.

Archaeologists are experts in _____

---

factory   history

satisfactory

unsatisfactory

compulsory

memory

laboratory

You must do this because it is _____.

"Your work is not good enough," said the manager. "It is very _____."

Cars are made in a _____.

Scientists work in a _____.

I have a very bad _____. I can't remember my tables.

---

transport

export   import

support

We _____ cars into this country, then we _____ them on car transporters.

You might like to _____ the camera on a tripod.

Step 1	Step 2	Step 3
Look and learn, then cover the word with the flap.	Write the word, then see if it's correct.	Write the word again. Say it as you write it.
biology		
biologist		
zoology		
zoologist		
geology		
geologist		
archaeology		
archaeologist		
science		
scientist		
scientific		
laboratory		
satisfactory		
unsatisfactory		
memory		
reporter		

Connectives

Connectives are words which can join two parts of a sentence together.

However, sometimes they can appear at the start of a sentence.

		word-bank		
whatever	whoever		whenever	if
although	since		alternatively	however
therefore	until	because	while	meanwhile	besides	consequently
	but	after	which	when	accordingly

Sort the words from the word-bank into alphabetical order.

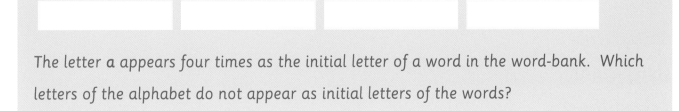

The letter **a** appears four times as the initial letter of a word in the word-bank. Which letters of the alphabet do not appear as initial letters of the words?

Step 1	Step 2	Step 3
Look and learn, then cover the word with the flap.	Write the word, then see if it's correct.	Write the word again. Say it as you write it.
however		
whatever		
whenever		
whoever		
alternative		
alternatively		
although		
while		
meanwhile		
because		
besides		
consequence		
consequently		
which		
according		
accordingly		

30

hydro, hydra, micro, trans

The prefixes hydra and hydro ...

... often show some connection with water or liquid.

Choose the correct word to fill each gap:

hydrofoil

hydroelectric

hydrogen

hydraulic

_____ power is electricity generated by the movement of water.

A _____ is a type of boat.

_____ is a gas.

_____ machines work by the movement of liquid.

microscope

microlight

microphone

microbiology

microwave

micro-organisms

We speak into a _____ .

We can cook with a _____ oven.

Very small creatures are called _____ .

We can see very small things with a _____ .

The study of micro-organisms is called _____ .

A _____ is a type of very small aeroplane.

The prefix **trans** means across or beyond. The word **transatlantic** means across or beyond the Atlantic Ocean. Practise these words which all begin with **trans**:

transport	transporter	transplant	transfer

transform	transparent	translate	transatlantic

31

Step 1	Step 2	Step 3
Look and learn, then cover the word with the flap.	Write the word, then see if it's correct.	Write the word again. Say it as you write it.
hydrogen		
hydrofoil		
hydraulic		
microscope		
microphone		
microwave		
microbiology		
transport		
transporter		
transform		
transformation		
transparent		
transparency		
transatlantic		
translate		
translation		

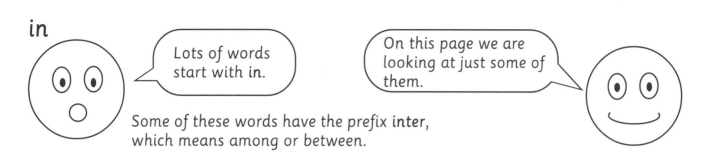

in

Lots of words start with **in**.

On this page we are looking at just some of them.

Some of these words have the prefix **inter**, which means among or between.

word-bank

inspect   international   inspector   interview
   inspection   intelligent   instant   intelligence
instantly   interrupt   intends   intention   intercept   inside   insert   insect
        inspire   interval   insertion   instead   interest   interested   interesting
introduce   instruct   introduction   instruction   instrument   insulation

Choose words from the word-bank to fill the gaps in these sentences:

I had to _____ the key into the lock.

I dropped the key so I couldn't get _____ .

Sally heard the boy playing a musical _____ .

The _____ came to inspect the school.

Dave asked me the score but I said I wasn't _____ in football.

Jasdeep is a very _____ girl. She _____ to be a doctor when she

grows up.

The new teacher had an _____ to get the job.

My teacher told me not to _____ her when she's talking.

When I went to the show I had an ice-cream in the _____ .

33

Step 1	Step 2	Step 3
Look and learn, then cover the word with the flap.	Write the word, then see if it's correct.	Write the word again. Say it as you write it.
inspect		
inspection		
instant		
instantly		
instruct		
instructor		
instructions		
instrument		
insulation		
international		
interest		
interesting		
interested		
introduce		
introducing		
introduction		

Other useful words

Sort the words in the word-bank …

… so that they are in word families.

word-bank

definite   mathematical   jewellers   minute
separately   vegetable   government   similar   maths
definition   secretary   journey   description   define   govern   mathematics
separate   jewellery   similarly   describe   vegetarian   definitely   jewels
secret   journalist   miniature   journal   similarity

definite

secret

similar

journey

jewels

describe

minute

maths

govern

separate

vegetable

Step 1	Step 2	Step 3
Look and learn, then cover the word with the flap.	Write the word, then see if it's correct.	Write the word again. Say it as you write it.
definite		
definitely		
definition		
separate		
separately		
govern		
government		
journey		
journalist		
jewellers		
jewellery		
similar		
similarly		
mathematics		
miniature		
description		